FEIFFER ON CIVIL RIGHTS

FOREWORD BY BAYARD RUSTIN

PUBLISHED BY THE ANTI-DEFAMATION LEAGUE OF B'NAI B'RITH

315 LEXINGTON AVENUE, NEW YORK, N.Y. 10016

Foreword

Introducing a collection of the work of one of the finest satirists and social critics of his generation is no easy task.

For one thing, my preface is in prose—in stolid, stodgy words that seek to be reasonable and judicious. And Jules Feiffer is the master of the comic epiphany, of that dramatic, illuminating moment which is both humorous and a more effective moral comment than any sermon one can imagine. And so, I find it extremely difficult to compress into some hundreds of words the meanings which Feiffer can explore in only six panels of a cartoon strip.

So it would be suicidal to try to paraphrase that which Feiffer has already said with a deftness and decisiveness which mocks those of us who attack injustice in conventional articles and speeches. But beyond this problem of bridging the chasm between our respective styles, there is another difficulty: Jules Feiffer was one of the very first to discover and identify that contemporary personality known as the "white liberal." That, I think, is what struck me most when I looked back over the work represented in this book. And that raises a most complicated, intricate subject, one that poses as many problems for the introducer as Feiffer's mastery of his art. Yet, I can only try to be equal to the candor and honesty of these drawings, so let me try to confront some of the significance of Feiffer's devastating critique.

In saying that Feiffer was one of the pioneers in defining the "white liberal," I don't mean that his work is obsessed by the theme or even that it dominates this selection. One meets the savage, unconscious white racist in this book, and the hip Negro who had to be cool simply in order to survive. And there is that marvelously touching account of the little white girl who is always getting caught in the middle of sit-ins. It took me back to the simple old days of three or four years ago when the basic issues seemed to be where people sat in busses or drank their coffee, that era of good feeling which perhaps culminated in the gigantic, and quite integrated March on Washington of 1963.

But since then, the questions of civil rights have become much more basic. They involve Northern urban neighborhood integration and *de facto* school segregation in communities which pay their respects to the liberal rhetoric. And there is the still unresolved question of jobs for black men who have been systematically deprived and mis-educated for generations and who are now told to go and "help themselves" in an automated economy which demands higher levels of skill and training every day. These miseries and indignities of the black ghetto poor no longer permit the Western movie version of the race issue as a struggle between the good guys and the bad rustlers from the Ku Klux Klan on the one side and the pious, churchgoing homesteaders on the other.

And Feiffer was one of the very first to understand that there were complexities—and even hypocrisies—in some of the attitudes of white liberalism. "Civil rights used to be so much more tolerable before Negroes got into it," declares one of his characters, and there is a wealth of insight in the comment. For only ten years ago, or was it five?—there was a tremendous amount of noblesse oblige, of Lord Bountiful, in the psychology of the best, the least racist, of whites.

Then there came the magnificent surge from below which took place in black America in recent years. It forever destroyed the myth that the passive Negro would gratefully accept his freedom from a well-intentioned, superior and somewhat self-righteous white. Suddenly Negroes—hundreds of thousands of them—got "into civil rights." I am the last one to argue that everything which was done by this vital, passionate movement was right. I would certainly not claim that black leadership is, by virtue of being black, necessarily more astute and intelligent than white. But I think that it is completely to the good that the exigencies of the struggle (and, above all, the courage of Negroes themselves) have made the old, benevolent approach of so much of white liberalism impossible. And, to state a point which I want to develop a little later on, it is extremely significant that a radical white critic was a premature analyst of this aspect of the white liberal personality.

So here you will meet the children of the dedicated, anti-racist parents who are sent to the exclusive suburban schools and that sinister Babbit, Mr. Whitey Backlash, who gives off-the-record interviews on a double standard that is becoming all too familiar in the North. These characters are pure Feiffer—and pure genius.

Secondly, there is one strip which I find a merciless, brilliant critique of all those (honest, sincere) people who tell the Negro to "help himself." This pompous, moralizing American knows that poverty, unemployment, drug addiction and crime are the simple free choice of the poor, the jobless, the junkie and the criminal. The six pictures are worth at least a dozen doctoral dissertations. For there are so many people who have no sense of the reality of Negro life. And to them, they stereotype the black, eighth generation American in his segregated ghetto in the midst of a cybernated economy as being the same as the aspiring, hopeful white immigrant of two generations ago who came into an America which could, and did, profitably put grade school dropouts to work. They do not understand, as Feiffer so obviously does, the massive social determinants which make the misery of poverty an infinitely more difficult fate to escape than ever before in our history. And then, of course. *no* group has ever faced a prejudice as profound as the one based on the color of a man's skin.

Finally, I think it is Feiffer's great merit to relate the issues of violence and non-violence to the society itself. The overt Southern racist, and Mr. Whitey Backlash—and, alas, some white liberals—propose a double standard. On the one hand, the society is to go on being as profoundly violent as it is, proclaiming that it is still necessary to recognize force as the supreme arbiter in international life and power as the decisive factor in the domestic economy. And on the other hand, these same people advise the Negro, who has suffered the very worst this nation has to give, to be non-violent, i.e., better than anyone else.

To me, it is remarkable that the American Negro has, to a considerable degree, achieved that act of transcendence. For this 10 percent minority of the American population has created the most effective non-violent mass movement since the time of Gandhi. development of that movement. And yet, at the same time, Feiffer is absolutely right to point out that the entire society is rotten-ripe with violence. If, then, I think it tragic when Negroes take up arms and strike out in riots and turmoil, I also think that it is understandable. During the first, booming half of the Sixties, when every occupational group advanced, the incomes of the people in Watts declined, their television sets told them of a world in which violence seems to be supreme. To reply to these people in pious sermons— to grandly tell them, as Mr. Whitey Backlash does, that "extremist tactics are losing the Negroes their many moderate friends"—is a vicious irrelevance.

But then does all this mean that I read Jules Feiffer as one more proof of the ultra-militant, nationalist point of view: white liberals are no good, violence is coming and that's fine, non-violence and integration are a fraud. That is not the point at all.

I think Jules Feiffer is absolutely right to expose the hypocrisies of white liberalism—and that his accomplishment in doing this is a triumph of the white liberal tradition. For if one can truthfully say, with Feiffer, that self-righteousness and self-congratulation have often been expressed by those who honestly, but incompetently, seek to fight for freedom, it is also true that there is a profound urge toward self-criticism, toward eventual honesty, among the partisans of social change. Today, a Negro writer like LeRoi Jones attacks Feiffer for being a white liberal—but yesterday, and even ten years ago, Feiffer was already dissecting the phony aspects that are to be found among white liberals. He was also exposing the hypocrisy of those Negro intellectuals who substitute verbal violence for participation in the movement and whose very lives and reputations depend on the masochistic adoration of white liberals.

I think, in short, that if the movement for integration can really learn Feiffer's lesson that there is great hope. The most decisive fact of the post-war period in America has been the growing consciousness of the black man—and things will never again be as they were. The Negro is going to organize, to select his leaders, he is going to *win* his freedom and not accept it from on high.

But the Negro minority cannot transform this powerful nation by itself. And as long as the white majority has its Jules Feiffers to unmask its pretenses, to criticize even the avowed advocates of justice and to do so ruthlessly—as long as we can talk as honestly as this book talks, there is hope of an integrated movement which will literally make a new America.

Bayard Rustin

IN THE OLD DAYS I USED TO GET INVITED TO THESE PARTIES—YOU KNOW—WHERE THE HOSTESS INSISTED THEY **HAD** TO BE **INTEGRATED**— YOU KNOW? SO THEY'D INVITE **ME**.

AND I'D ALWAYS MEET A WHOLE BUNCH OF OFFICIAL-FRIENDLY PEOPLE—YOU KNOW— **GUYS** WITH **STRONG** HAND SHAKES, **CHICKS** WHO **HAD** TO DANCE WITH ME. IT'S NOT EASY BEING ROBBED OF A CHOICE WHEN THE GIRL IS UGLY.

AND SOONER OR LATER A COUPLE OF THESE CATS WOULD GET ME IN A CORNER AND — WE'D ALL BLOW SMOKE AT EACH OTHER AND BE **ENLIGHTENED** — AND THEY'D WANT TO TALK ABOUT CIVIL RIGHTS UNDER THE DEMOCRATS BECAUSE THERE'S NOTHING A LIBERAL LOVES BETTER THAN BEING MADE TO **FEEL GUILTY** - BUT I WOULDN'T **TOUCH** IT — I'D TALK ABOUT MY **CAR** AND **BASEBALL** AND HOW **DULL** FOREIGN MOVIES ARE.

UNTIL THEY GOT SO JUMPY THAT **ONE** OF THEM **HAD** TO BRING "IT" UP. AND I'D PRETEND TO BE **SURPRISED** THAT THEY'D BE INTERESTED IN **MY** PROBLEMS. BUT THEY INSISTED THAT BEING MEMBERS OF THE **A.D.A.** THEY CON- SIDERED IT **EVERY- BODY'S** PROBLEM.

SO I ONLY SAID I
DIDN'T **LOOK ON**
CIVIL RIGHTS AS
A "**HUMANIST**"
ISSUE. THE WAY **I**
LOOKED AT IT- IT
WAS STRICTLY
SELF-INTEREST.
YOU KNOW—LIKE
IT'S BEEN A LONG
WAIT AND **I**
WANT **MINE**.

SO A COUPLE OF THEM, HERE
AND THERE, GOT **RESTLESS**
ABOUT WHAT THEY CALLED
MY "**EXTREMIST**" ATTITUDE.
BUT ALL THE WHILE THEY
KEPT **SMILING.** AS
A PEOPLE I FIND
LIBERALS VERY
GOOD NATURED.

BUT THE PARTY ALWAYS BROKE UP ABOUT AN HOUR EARLY AND I COULD SEE **NOBODY** REALLY GOT WHAT THEY **CAME** FOR— EXCEPT **ME.** I FELT I WAS SUBTLY PUSHING A FASTER RATE OF SOCIAL INTEGRATION. AND I WAS **RIGHT.**

AT THEIR NEXT PARTY THEY HAD **TWO** NEGROES— JUST IN CASE THE FIRST ONE DIDN'T WORK OUT.

SO MOMMA AND I GOT ON THIS BUS TO GO TO THE COUNTRY AND SUDDENLY A BUNCH OF COLORED PEOPLE GOT ON AND WE WERE SURROUNDED BY POLICEMEN AND WE ALL GOT ARRESTED.

MOMMA **TRIED** TO TELL THE POLICEMEN WE WERE ONLY GOING TO THE COUNTRY BUT ALL THE COLORED PEOPLE WERE SINGING "**WE SHALL OVERCOME**" SO THE POLICEMEN COULDN'T HEAR US.

SO AFTER DADDY GOT US OUT OF JAIL MOMMA AND I WENT TO GET A **SANDWICH** IN A **DRUG-STORE** BEFORE WE TRIED AGAIN TO GO TO THE COUNTRY — AND SUDDENLY A BUNCH OF COLORED PEOPLE WERE SITTING ON STOOLS ALL AROUND US AND WE WERE SURROUNDED BY POLICEMEN AND WE ALL GOT ARRESTED.

MOMMA **TRIED** TO TELL THE POLICE-MEN WE WERE ONLY TRYING TO **EAT** AND **GO TO THE COUNTRY** BUT ALL THE COLORED PEOPLE WERE SINGING "**WE SHALL OVERCOME**" SO THE POLICEMEN COULDN'T HEAR US.

SO AFTER DADDY GOT US OUT OF JAIL WE **RENTED** A CAR TO THE COUNTRY AND MOMMA WAS SO RELIEVED THAT BEFORE EVEN **UNPACKING** SHE TOOK ME DOWN TO THE BEACH TO RELAX AND SUN BATHE AND SUDDENLY A BUNCH OF COLORED PEOPLE WERE SUN BATHING ALL AROUND US AND THE POLICEMEN CAME AND WE ALL GOT ARRESTED.

MOMMA **TRIED** TO TELL THE POLICE-
MEN WE WERE ONLY TRYING TO
SUN BATHE BUT ALL THE COLORED
PEOPLE AND ME WERE
SINGING " **WE SHALL
OVERCOME** " SO THEY
TOOK US TO JAIL.

I DON'T MIND THE COLORED
PEOPLE BUT I WISH THEY'D
LEAVE THEIR POLICEMEN HOME.

DON'T GET ME WRONG. I UNDERSTAND WHAT YOU'RE TRYING TO DO. BUT I CAN'T TAKE YOU TO WORK WITH ME.
HAVE YOU EVER TAKEN A COLORED PERSON TO WORK WITH YOU?
BELIEVE ME, I WOULD IF I FOUND ONE QUALIFIED. I'M ON YOUR SIDE. YOU DON'T WANT ME!
WONDERFUL. WE CAN DISCUSS IT AT WORK.
LOOK, I DO MY BIT! EVERY DAY I DELIBERATELY SIT NEXT TO ONE OF YOU ON THE BUS! DON'T I GET SOME TIME OFF FOR LIBERALISM?
HAVE YOU EVER TAKEN A COLORED PERSON HOME WITH YOU?

EVER SINCE HE WAS KNEE HIGH
TO A GRASS HOPPER I'D SAY
TO LITTLE BEN, "LITTLE
BEN, YOU'RE SHIFTLESS
AN' LAZY," AN' LITTLE
BEN WOULD SHUFFLE
A STEP OR TWO
AN' SAY "GUESS
I IS, MR. TOM."
WE GOT ALONG
FINE THAT WAY,
LITTLE BEN AN' ME.

I'D KEEP TELLIN'
HIM WHAT HE
WAS AN' SURE
ENOUGH HE
COME T'BE
THAT WAY.

AN' HE WAS GROWIN'
UP JES' FINE TILL
THEM OUTSIDERS
COME ALONG AN'
TOLD LITTLE BEN
JES' BECAUSE
I TOLD HIM
HE WAS SHIFT-
LESS AN' LAZY
DIDN'T MAKE
IT SO.

WELL, AFTER THAT LITTLE BEN DIDN'T LISTEN TO ME THE WAY HE USE' TO. I'D SAY, "LITTLE BEN, NO MATTER WHAT ANYBODY SAYS, YOU'RE SHIFTLESS AN' LAZY AN' TOTALLY DEVOTED T'ME."

AN' HE'D SASS RIGHT BACK WITH, "MR. TOM, NO MATTER WHAT ANYBODY SAYS, YOU'RE A RACIST, YOU'RE A KILLER AN' YOUR TIME IS COMIN'."

WELL, I BEAT HIM UP PRETTY GOOD FOR THAT AN' ANYTIME I'D SEE MORE AGITATORS AROUND I TOOK A GUN TO THEM. BUT IT DIDN'T DO NO GOOD.

I BEGUN T'WORRY IF I WASN'T LIKE WHAT LITTLE BEN SAID.

SO I KILLED LITTLE BEN.

THAT'S WHAT HE GETS FOR MAK-IN' ME BELIEVE HIS DREAM INSTEAD O' HIS BELIEVIN' MINE.

 I FLED TO FREEDOM FROM EAST GERMANY. DON'T LOOK AT ME THAT WAY. I SAY **I DID!**

 SO I GOT ACROSS THE BORDER AND THE ALLIED OFFICERS SAID, " MAN, WHAT ARE **YOU** DOING?" AND I SAID "YOU CAN SEE PLAIN WELL WHAT I'M DOING. I'M FLEEING TO FREEDOM."

 "WELL, MAN, HOW CAN YOU FLEE TO FREEDOM?" THEY ASKED ME. "YOU GERMAN?" AND I REPLIED "NO SIR." "YOU CHINESE?" AND I REPLIED, "NO SIR." "YOU RUSSIAN, HUNGARIAN, ALBANIAN, CZECH, POLE, **SI**BERIAN?" AND TO ALL THAT STUFF I REPLIED "NO SIR." "WELL, THEN," THEY SAID "YOU **CAN'T** BE FLEEING TO FREEDOM."

BUT I WOULDN'T GO BACK
SO THEY HAD TO FIGURE
OUT WHERE TO SEND ME.
THE FRENCH OFFICER
SAID "MAN, WE **CAN'T**
SEND YOU TO FRANCE.
YOU MIGHT GET PICKED
OFF AS AN ALGERIAN."

THE ENGLISH OFFICER SAID,
"WE ALREADY GOT OUR
TROUBLES IN **LONDON**—
AND SOUTH AFRICA
WOULDN'T HAVE YOU.
AND WE AREN'T LIKELY
TO SEND YOU ANY-
WHERES **ELSE** IN
AFRICA BECAUSE FOR
ALL **WE** KNOW YOU
COULD BE A KENYATTA
OR SOMETHING."

AND THE AMERICAN OFFICER
SAID, "WE **CAN'T** SEND
YOU TO THE **SOUTH**
BECAUSE IF YOU
FLED TO FREEDOM
ONCE, WHAT'S TO
STOP YOU FROM
BEING A TROUBLE
MAKER AND TRYING
IT AGAIN?

-AND WE CAN'T SEND YOU TO CUBA BECAUSE THAT'S NO LONGER PART OF THE **FREE WORLD**. THEY REPRESS WHITE FOLKS THERE **TOO**." SO THEY ALL SAID, "WHY DON'T YOU BE A GOOD FELLOW AND GO BACK WHERE YOU CAME FROM?"

WELL, I DON'T KNOW, MAYBE I WILL.

DURING A MORAL CRISIS BETWIXT FREEDOM AND SLAVERY I DON'T WANT TO BE THE ONE TO MAKE TROUBLE.

YOU SEE WHAT THE PROBLEM **IS**, A LOT OF THESE **NEW** COUNTRIES ARE COLORED AND THEY'RE- YOU **KNOW**- VERY OVER SENSITIVE.

BOY, DON'T I **KNOW!** YOU SHOULD SPEAK TO THE GIRL I HAVE COME IN ON MONDAYS.

AND I DON'T HAVE TO TELL YOU THE WAY IT IS - THEY DON'T HAVE OUR WEALTH OF **EXPERIENCE** - I MEAN BASICALLY THEY'RE A VERY **INNOCENT** PEOPLE - I MEAN - **THEY'RE** NOT SOPHISTICATED!

WELL, YOU'RE EITHER OR YOU'RE NOT I SAY.

THEN THEY COME TO THE UNITED NATIONS IN NEW YORK AND THEY EXPECT EVERYBODY TO BE THEIR **FRIEND**. THEY DON'T UNDERSTAND ABOUT NEW YORK. NOBODY'S **ANYBODY'S** FRIEND.

CAN YOU **IMAGINE**? THEY'RE VERY INNOCENT IF YOU ASK ME.

SO IF THEY GET TREATED NASTY IN A RESTAURANT OR FOR INSTANCE GET SHOVED IN THE STREET THEY THINK IT'S BECAUSE WE DON'T **RESPECT** THEM.

WELL I'VE DISCOVERED AFTER A LONG LIFE THAT YOU HAVE TO **EARN** RESPECT. IF YOU'RE NOT IN **TOO** MUCH OF A HURRY — IF YOU KNOW YOUR PL—

BUT YOU DON'T UNDER-
STAND! DON'T YOU SEE
THEY ALL HAVE CHIPS ON
THEIR SHOULDER! SO
NOW IT LOOKS LIKE
IF WE DON'T
SERVE THEM
NICE IN OUR
RESTAURANTS,
THEY'LL
ALL GO
COMMUNIST.

COMMUNIST!
AND I USED TO
THINK THEY WERE
ALL SO GOOD-
NATURED. WELL YOU
TURN YOUR
BACK ON
PEOPLE
FOR A
MINUTE
AND—

SO RATHER THAN LET THEM
GO COMMUNIST I SUPPOSE
ITS OUR DUTY TO HELP THEM—
BUT AFTER ALL IT'S A HARD
LIFE FOR EVERYBODY. I MY-
SELF DON'T ALWAYS
GET THE BEST SERVICE
IN RESTAURANTS. BUT
I'M A GOOD SPORT.
I LAUGH IT OFF.

AFRICA WOULD
BE A LOT
BETTER OFF IF
IT WAS MORE
LIKE YOU, DORIS.

SO I SAID TO HIM:
"YOU'RE ON THE
WRONG TRACK,
PHIL. MAN IS
NOT BASICALLY
EVIL. MAN IS
NEITHER BASICALLY
GOOD NOR **EVIL.**"

PERFECTLY
REASONABLE.

I SAID TO HIM: "YOU'RE
OVER-SIMPLIFYING
PHIL. NO ONE DENIES
THAT MAN COMMITS
GREAT SINS. BUT **DON'T**
JUST LOOK ON THE
DARK SIDE. LOOK AT
THE FORCE FOR
GOOD HE'S BEEN."

PERFECTLY
REASONABLE.

I SAID TO HIM "YOU'RE **OVERLY-ANALYTICAL**, PHIL. MAN DOESN'T DO GOOD TO ALLEVIATE SOME FANCIED SENSE OF GUILT AS **YOU** THINK. WHEN MAN DOES GOOD ITS BECAUSE HE **IS** GOOD. WHEN MAN DOES EVIL ITS BECAUSE **SOCIETY** HAS MADE HIM THAT WAY."

PERFECTLY REASONABLE.

I SAID TO HIM : "YOU'RE TOO MUCH THE PESSIMIST, PHIL. CERTAINLY, WE MOVE **SLOWLY**, BUT IF **ALL** OF US IN OUR **OWN** LIVES MAKE AS GOOD A JOB OF IT AS WE CAN — AS PARENTS, AS TEACHERS, AS BUSINESS MEN, AS CITIZENS — THEN LITTLE BY LITTLE THE WORLD **HAS** TO BECOME A BETTER PLACE TO LIVE IN."

PERFECTLY REASONABLE.

NOT ACCORDING TO
PHIL. HE LAUGHED
IN MY FACE AND –
CALLED ME AN
IDIOT-LIBERAL!

HOW AWFUL! WHAT
DID YOU DO?

WHAT
COULD
I DO? –
I
KILLED
HIM.

PERFECTLY
REASONABLE.

BILLIE CAME OVER TO ME IN THE MORNING AND SAID YOU PROMISED TO TAKE ME TO THE ZOO TODAY, DADDY. AND I SAID I'M SORRY BILLIE-BOY BUT DADDY HAS GOT SOMETHING ELSE HE MUST DO TODAY.

AND BILLIE'S MOMMA SAID NOW YOU STOP BOTHERING YOUR DADDY, BILLIE-BOY. AND I SAID DON'T SCOLD THE BOY, CHARLOTTE. I KNOW JUST THE WAY HE FEELS BECAUSE I STILL REMEMBER WHAT IT WAS LIKE WHEN **MY** DADDY DISAPPOINTED **ME**.

AND CHARLOTTE HUGGED ME
AND CALLED ME HER HONEY-
BEAR AND SAID YOU'RE TOO
GENTLE FOR YOUR OWN
GOOD, DANNY. AND I
SAID IT'S A BAD THING
WHEN A FATHER HAS TO
BREAK A PROMISE TO HIS
SON. THAT'S THE WAY
A CHILD CAN TURN SOUR.

AND CHARLOTTE SAID NO
CHILD OF OURS WILL TURN
SOUR SO LONG AS A MAN
LIKE YOU IS AROUND. AND
I HUGGED HER AND SAID
YOU'RE MY LITTLE GIRL.
THEN I PICKED UP MY
BAT AND I SAID I'D
BEST BE ON MY WAY.
I'M LATE AS IT IS.

HIT ONE FOR ME,
CHARLOTTE YELLED.
AND FOR ME TOO,
DADDY, BILLIE-BOY
YELLED. AND I
YELLED BACK
DON'T YOU WORRY
ABOUT ME. I'LL
DO FINE.

AND THEN I
DROVE DOWN-
TOWN TO THE
CIVIL RIGHTS
DEMONSTRATION.

THE ISSUE OF MOB VIOLENCE AND ITS RELATION TO OUR EDUCATION SYSTEM HAS RAISED A NUMBER OF INTERESTING QUESTIONS.

WE ALL AGREE THAT THE ROLE OF THE EDU-CATOR IS NOT ONLY TO TEACH HIS SUBJECT BUT TO IMPART AN UNDERSTANDING OF MORAL VALUES.

BUT ONE CAN NOT PUSH A STUDENT BEYOND THE POINT HE IS WILLING TO GO. ONE MUST WORK WITHIN THE **SPIRIT** OF HIS **CULTURE**. THE SPIRIT OF **OUR** CULTURE IS **LATENT VIOLENCE.**

THOUGH ACHIEVING TEMPORARY RELEASE THROUGH TELEVISION PROGRAMS AND NEWSPAPER HEADLINES, THIS SPIRIT MUST OCCASIONALLY FIND A **DIRECT** OUTLET. MURDER WON'T DO. IT LOSES ONE THE RESPECT OF HIS NEIGHBORS.

HOWEVER, MOB VIOLENCE WILL DO **PERFECTLY.** HOW CAN ONE LOSE THE RESPECT OF HIS NEIGHBORS IF THEY **TOO** ARE BURNING AUTOMOBILES?

OUR PROBLEM THEN IS THAT,
WHILE IT MAY BE ALL TO
THE GOOD TO LECTURE
AGAINST THE SPIRIT OF
LATENT VIOLENCE, IS IT
DESIRABLE TO LECTURE
THAT SPIRIT INTO
EXTINCTION?

CAN ONE BLANKETLY
CONDEMN A SPIRIT
WHICH IN ITS MORE
ORGANIZED FORM
IS DEPENDED ON
TO DEFEND THE
FREE WORLD?

SO OUR BASIC QUESTION
REMAINS : IF WE
ROB MEN OF
THEIR DESIRE
TO TAKE THE
UNIVERSITY OF
MISSISSIPPI,
DO WE ALSO
ROB THEM OF
THEIR DESIRE
TO TAKE CUBA?

IT IS NOT EASY
TO TEACH IN
THE TWENTIETH
CENTURY.

MY FATHER SAYS THAT
"THANK GOD, IT'S A
BLESSING WE DON'T
LIVE IN THE SOUTH
WITH ALL THIS
GOING ON."

ABSOLUTELY.
MY FATHER
AGREES.

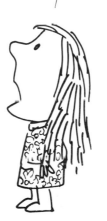

MY FATHER SAYS "HA! AND
THEY CALL THIS A **DEMOCRACY!**
DON'T THEY KNOW HOW THIS
LOOKS TO THE UNCOMMITTED
COUNTRIES?"

EXACTLY WHAT MY
FATHER SAYS. MY
FATHER IS VERY
INTERESTED IN
UNCOMMITTED
COUNTRIES.

MY FATHER SAYS, "I'M ASHAMED TO CALL MYSELF AN AMERICAN WITH LITTLE ROCK AND ALL."

MY FATHER QUITE DEFINITELY AGREES. HE'S ALWAYS BEING ASHAMED OF CALLING HIMSELF AN AMERICAN.

MY FATHER SAYS THAT, "THANK GOD THERE'S NONE OF THIS NONSENSE HERE IN NEW YORK."

MY FATHER GOES RIGHT ALONG WITH YOUR FATHER. THEY CAN THROW THE REST OF THE COUNTRY AWAY AS FAR AS MY FATHER IS CONCERNED.

WITH US TONIGHT TO GIVE HIS
VIEWS ON THE CURRENT RACIAL
CRISIS, IS A SPOKESMAN FOR
THAT GROUP WE HEAR MORE
AND MORE FROM THESE DAYS-
THE **RADICAL MIDDLE**.

VERY
SERIOUS.
EXTREMELY
GRAVE.
DEEPLY
DISTURBING.

AS I UNDERSTAND YOUR
GROUP, SIR, IT ADVOCATES
AN IRRESPONSIBLE
MIDDLE POSITION. IS
THAT CORRECT?

YES AND NO. FOR INSTANCE
IN THE FIELD OF LABOR
WE HAVE TRADITONALLY
RECOGNIZED THE RIGHT TO
ORGANIZE WHILE BEING
TRADITIONALLY CRITI-
CAL OF THE
NEED TO
STRIKE.

OR, IN THE FIELD OF CIVIL LIBERTIES — WE HAVE TRADITIONALLY FAVORED THE BILL OF RIGHTS WHILE BEING TRADITIONALLY CRITICAL OF ITS ACROSS-THE-BOARD IMPLEMENTATION.

AND SO, TODAY IN THE FIELD OF CIVIL RIGHTS. WE TRADITIONALLY RECOGNIZE THE NEGROES' RIGHT TO PROTEST WHILE BEING TRADITIONALLY OPPOSED TO LEGISLATIVE CONCESSIONS WON BY PUBLIC DEMAND.

THEN SIR, YOUR ADVICE WOULD BE —

CONCILIATION. RESPONSIBLE MODERATES FROM BOTH SIDES SHOULD MEET AND MEET AND MEET UNTIL THEY NAIL DOWN FIRM PROPOSALS ON WHICH ALL MEN OF GOOD WILL CAN UNANIMOUSLY AGREE.

BUT, SIR, WON'T THAT TAKE **YEARS**?

I CAN WAIT.

AS PART OF A FACT FINDING,
TROUBLE SHOOTING PRESIDENTIAL
TEAM SENT OUT TO SEEK
WAYS OF RESTORING
BI-RACIAL COMMUNI-
CATIONS IN SOUTHERN
CITIES, I WOULD LIKE
TO REPORT OUR
FINDINGS.

NO. 1- IT IS OUR CONCLUSION THAT SOME OF
THE DIFFICULTIES ARE **SEMANTIC**. THE NEGRO
COMMUNITY HAS DROPPED THE USE OF
THE COURTESY WORD "SIR," REPLACING
IT WITH A WORD FOUND TO BE FAR
LESS APPEALING. IMMEDIATE
REINSTATEMENT OF THE WORD
"SIR" MIGHT WELL OPEN **OTHER**
AREAS FOR DISCUSSION.

NO. 2- IN TALKS WITH WHITE CIVIC LEADERS IT BECAME CLEAR THAT INCREASED TENSION WAS DUE TO NEGRO LAPSES IN THE TECHNIQUE OF NON-VIOLENCE. SOUTHERN MODERATES FEEL THIS TO BE A **BETRAYAL** OF THE NEGRO REVOLUTION AND INSIST THAT ONCE THE NEGRO COMMUNITY SURRENDERS ITS ARMS, OTHER AREAS FOR DISCUSSION MIGHT WELL BE OPENED.

NO. 3- SOUTHERN MODERATES DEEM THE CONTINUED INVOLVEMENT OF NEGRO CHILDREN IN **SUNDAY SCHOOLS** TO BE A **DELIBERATE PROVOCATION.** RETURN NEGRO RELIGION TO THE HARMLESS PURPOSES IT WAS DESIGNED FOR AND **OTHER** AREAS FOR DISCUSSION MIGHT WELL BE OPENED.

FINALLY WE FIND THAT WHITE CIVIC
LEADERS REMAIN PERTURBED AT
OUTSIDE AGITATORS - A PRIME
EXAMPLE BEING THEIR ANGER
AT OUR FACT FINDING, TROUBLE
SHOOTING PRESIDENTIAL TEAM
WHEN IT TRIED TO GET IN TOUCH
WITH THE NEGRO COMMUNITY.
THE DISSOLUTION OF OUR TEAM
MIGHT WELL SERVE TO OPEN
OTHER AREAS FOR DISCUSSION.

OUR PRESENT ATTITUDE
IS THAT THIS MEANINGFUL
DIALOGUE SHOULD BE
CONTINUED.

THE F.B.I. WORKS HAND IN PAW WITH LOCAL LAW ENFORCEMENT DOGS. COME ALONG, QUIETLY.

I KNOW MY RIGHTS. I'LL GO THROUGH THE COURTS.

THE COURTS TAKE **FOREVER**. WHY ELSE WOULD WE ENCOURAGE YOU TO USE THEM? COME ALONG, QUIETLY.

I KNOW MY RIGHTS. I'LL PICKET NON-VIOLENTLY.

NON-VIOLENCE MAY
MAKE US FEEL GUILTY
BUT WE CAN LEARN
TO LIVE WITH IT.
COME ALONG QU—
HEY— WHAT DO YOU
THINK **YOU'RE** DOING?

WHAT DOES
IT **LOOK**
LIKE I'M
DOING?

TELL ME— WHAT IS IT
YOU PEOPLE WANT?

ALL MY LIFE PEOPLE
BEEN TELLING ME I
HAVE A MORAL OBLIGATION.

BEFORE THE WAR I
HAD A MORAL
OBLIGATION TO
FIGHT FASCISM.

DURING THE WAR I **OWED** IT TO MY COUNTRY TO **JOIN THE ARMY.**

AFTER THE WAR IT WAS MY **DUTY** TO WORK FOR **PEACE, INTEGRATION, DECENT HOUSING** AND **BETTER TELEVISION PROGRAMS.**

SO I CAN'T BE **FOR** SOMETHING BECAUSE IT'S JUST **RIGHT** ANYMORE. I GOT TO BE FOR IT BECAUSE I'D **OWE** SOMEBODY IF I WASN'T.

I FEEL AS IF I'M LIVING IN A MORAL DEBTORS' PRISON.

HOW'S IT BEEN — THIS YEAR?

ROUGH. EVER SINCE THE ECUMENICAL COUNCIL WE'VE HAD NOTHING BUT THESE JEWISH GIRLS TRYING TO GET INTO OUR SORORITY.

WHAT DO YOU TELL THEM? —

WHAT **CAN** YOU TELL THEM? YOU OPEN YOUR **MOUTH** TO EXPLAIN AND THEY CALL YOU ANTI-SEMETIC.

WHAT ROT! **NOBODY** DOES ANTI-SEMITISM ANYMORE. IT'S **PASSÉ**. IF WE'RE ANTI-ANYTHING THESE DAYS, IT'S **NEGRO**.

WELL, HOW WOULD **THEY** KNOW? THEY DON'T KEEP UP. THEY'RE TOO BUSY **READING** — OR WHAT-EVER IT IS THEY DO.

WE HAD A COUPLE OF THEM OVER TO OUR MIXER — AND THEY WERE SO ANXIOUS TO BE LIKED IT WAS **EMBAR-RASSING!**

I KNOW! THEY THINK ALL IT TAKES IS TO BE **NICE!** IT'S LIKE WE SPEAK DIFFER-ENT LANGUAGES, REALLY!

WELL, HOW DO YOU **HANDLE** IT— NOW THAT THEY'VE BEEN JUDGED "**NOT GUILTY**"?

WE SIMPLY TELL THEM IT DOESN'T APPLY TO US.

AFTER ALL, WE DON'T TAKE CATHOLICS EITHER.

USED TO GO TO
THE VAUDEVILLE
HOUSE - HEAR
A GOOD
RASTUS -
MANDY STORY.
EVERYONE
LOVED 'EM!
NOBODY
TOOK IT
WRONG.

TRY TO
TELL ONE
TODAY -
EVERYONE'S
OFFENDED.

USED TO GO
TO PARTIES -
STAYED UP ALL
NIGHT TELLING
HYMIE - ABIE
STORIES.
LAUGHED? WE
COULDA **DIED!**
IT WAS ALL
IN FUN.

TRY TO
TELL ONE
TODAY -
EVERYONE
GETS
OFFENDED.

USED TO GET
TOGETHER
AFTER A STAG
MOVIE AND
TELL MICK
JOKES,
CHINAMAN
JOKES,
POLACK JOKES,
LIMEY JOKES,
FROG JOKES-
A **MILLION**
LAUGHS!

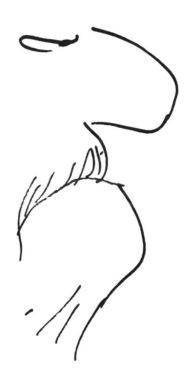

TRY TO
TELL 'EM
TODAY-
YOU GET
YOUR
HEAD
BUSTED.

USED TO DO THIS IMITATION OF A GUY WITH A BAD LEG. A **REGULAR RIOT!** TRY TO IMITATE A CRIPPLE TODAY— SEE WHAT IT GETS YOU!

HUMOR IS DEAD IN THIS COUNTRY.

I DON'T KNOW IF I CAN GO WITH A BOY UNLESS I KNOW HOW HE FEELS ABOUT **IMPORTANT** THINGS, HENRY— **WORLDLY** THINGS —

TEST ME— ASK ME **ANYTHING**, LUCILLE! **I'M** WELL READ!

WELL, HOW WOULD YOU DESCRIBE YOURSELF **POLITICALLY**?

I'VE GIVEN THAT A **LOT** OF THOUGHT AND AFTER WEIGHING THE ADVANTAGES OF **BOTH** PARTIES I'D SAY I WAS AN **INDEPENDENT**.

WHERE DO
YOU STAND
ON THE
INTEGRATION
ISSUE?

WELL, AFTER CONSID-
ERING ALL THE
PROS AND CONS
I THINK-AT LEAST
TENTATIVELY-THAT
I'D HAVE TO GO
ALONG WITH THE
SUPREME COURT.
IT **IS** THE LAW
OF THE LAND.

AND WHERE
DO YOU
STAND ON
THE CIVIL
LIBERTIES
ISSUE?

WELL, NONE OF US
CAN BE **REALLY**
SURE OF WHAT'S
GOING ON, BUT
AFTER EXAMIN-
ING THOSE
FACTS AVAIL-
ABLE TO THE
PUBLIC I'D
HAVE TO AGREE
WITH THE SU-
PREME COURT.
IT **IS** THE LAW
OF THE LAND.

AND THE
SCHOOL
PRAYER
ISSUE?

NOW I'VE GONE INTO
THIS QUESTION
RATHER EXTENSIVE-
LY AND WHILE
THERE IS MERIT
IN EVERY OPINION
I'VE HEARD – I'M
FORCED TO
AGREE WITH THE
SUPREME COURT.
IT **IS** THE LAW
OF THE LAND.

I THINK IT'S BETTER
THAT WE DON'T
SEE EACH
OTHER
AGAIN,
HENRY.

BUT **WHY**
LUCILLE?
WHY?

I NEVER DREAMED
YOU WERE
A RADICAL!

WE ON THE RIGHT ARE
AT A LOSS TO UNDER-
STAND THE MEANING
OF THE WORD "RADICAL"
AS USED IN THE PHRASE,
"RADICAL RIGHT."

THE TERM "RADICAL"
IN THIS CONTEXT CAN
ONLY BE DEFENDED
WHEN APPLIED TO
WHAT OUR SOCIETY
PRETENDS TO BE,
NOT WHAT IT IS.

AFTER ALL, DOES NOT THE
RADICAL RIGHT STAND FOR
PRINCIPLES THAT MOST
AMERICANS, ONCE THEY
ARE **COMFORTABLE**,
GENERALLY SUPPORT: —

i.e.; "I'VE GOT MINE,
YOU GET YOURS" ?

RECENT POLLS CITING NORTHERN
WHITE REACTION TO THE CIVIL-
RIGHTS MOVEMENT ILLUSTRATE
HOW LITTLE THE NATION IS
INTERESTED IN EQUALITY WHEN
A MIDDLE-CLASS, WHITE CROSS
SECTION IS NOT INVOLVED.

SO THE RADICAL RIGHT'S PROGRAM IN THE INTEGRATION FIELD DOES NOT DIFFER FROM THE **REAL** DESIRES OF THE MAN ON THE STREET. HOWEVER, IT **DOES** DIFFER FROM WHAT THE MAN ON THE STREET HAS BEEN **TAUGHT** HE SHOULD DESIRE.

IN THIS CASE, AND OTHERS, THE RADICAL RIGHT CAN BE CALLED "RADICAL" ONLY IN THE SENSE THAT IT DEPARTS FROM OUR **OFFICIAL** BELIEFS, NOT OUR **PRIVATE** ONES.

ONCE WE GET PEOPLE TO VOTE **EMOTIONALLY** INSTEAD OF **RATIONALLY** WE WILL WIN IN A LANDSLIDE.

WHEN MY HUSBAND BEGAN TO BUILD OUR SHELTER HE WAS GOING TO BUILD **TWO** OF THEM. ONE FOR THE FAMILY AND ONE FOR OUR **HIRED GIRL**. SAME DIMENSIONS, SAME MATERIAL, EXACTLY LIKE OURS IN EVERY DETAIL.

WHY NOT. THEY EXPECT YOUR **BLOOD** THESE DAYS.

WELL **YOU** SHOULD HAVE HEARD THAT GIRL TALK WHEN I TOLD HER THE NEWS. I DON'T KNOW **WHERE** SHE PICKED UP SOME OF THE **IDEAS** SHE HAS. SHE'S BEEN WITH US TEN YEARS AND NEVER HAD THEM **BEFORE**.

A LOT OF THEM ARE SECRETLY VERY FRESH.

WELL YOU CAN'T ARGUE WITH A STUBBORN MIND SO WE **GAVE** IN. GOOD GIRLS ARE TOO HARD TO GET THESE DAYS. SO I TOLD HER THAT OUR FAMILY WAS WILLING TO ABIDE BY THE LAW OF THE LAND AND DURING THE NEXT ALERT SHE COULD JOIN US IN OUR SHELTER.

YOU'RE MORE FAIR THAN A LOT OF PEOPLE WOULD HAVE BEEN, I'LL TELL YOU **THAT**.

WELL, ON HER DAY OFF A FEW WEEKS **AFTER** THAT, I WAS HOME WATCHING THE U.N. ON TELEVISION— BECAUSE YOU NEVER KNOW WHEN ONE OF THOSE STRANGE SOUNDING DELEGATES NAMES IS GOING TO SHOW UP IN A CROSS-WORD PUZZLE.

YOU DON'T HAVE TO EXPLAIN. **I** UNDERSTAND.

AND SUDDENLY THERE **SHE** IS - **OUR** GIRL AT THE U.N. - **RIOTING!** WELL YOU CAN IMAGINE I HAD A **FEW** WORDS READY FOR **HER** WHEN SHE CAME BACK TO WORK! BUT BEFORE I COULD OPEN MY MOUTH SHE SPOKE UP FIRST - SHE HAD **CHANGED** HER MIND - SHE WOULD NOT **SHARE** OUR IMPERIALIST AIR RAID SHELTER! SHE WAS NOW A **NEUTRALIST** AND WANTED A **SEPARATE** AIR RAID SHELTER.

WHAT NERVE! FORCE HER TO SHARE IT! SHE CAN'T DO THAT TO **YOU!**

OH, WE TRIED. WE LECTURED HER ABOUT DEMOCRACY AND QUOTED ABRAHAM LINCOLN BUT IN THE END WE HAD TO BUILD A SHELTER FOR US AND A SHELTER FOR **HER**. GOOD GIRLS ARE TOO HARD TO FIND THESE DAYS.

THE GOVERNMENT SHOULD **DO** SOMETHING. **YOU** WATCH! **NEXT** THEY'LL REFUSE TO GO TO OUR SCHOOLS.

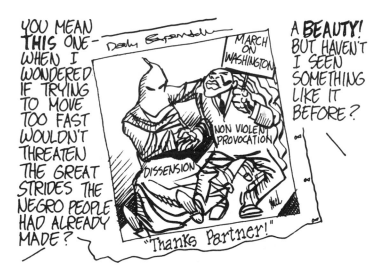

EVERYBODY HAS A CHOICE. YOU WOULDN'T HAVE — TO BE POOR IF YOU DIDN'T **WANT** TO BE.

IT'S A FREE COUNTRY. YOU WOULDN'T — HAVE TO BE UNEMPLOYED IF YOU DIDN'T **WANT** TO BE.

THIS IS THE
LAND OF
OPPORTUNITY.
YOU WOULDN'T
HAVE TO BE
BADLY EDU-
CATED IF YOU
DIDN'T **WANT**
TO BE.

EVERY BOY
CAN BE PRES-
IDENT. YOU
WOULDN'T
HAVE TO BE
AN ADDICT
IF YOU DIDN'T
WANT TO BE.

ALL IT TAKES
IS INITIATIVE.
YOU WOULDN'T
HAVE TO TURN
TO CRIME IF
YOU DIDN'T
WANT IT TO BE.

EVERYBODY HAS A CHOICE.
I WOULDN'T HAVE TO BE
DEAD IF I DIDN'T **WANT** TO BE.

YOU'RE THROUGH WHITEY! FINISHED! DEAD! A REVOLUTION IS SWEEPING THE WORLD AND YOU'RE OUT OF IT!
NOTHING YOU CAN DO TO SAVE YOURSELF, WHITEY! DON'T OFFER ME YOUR WHITE MARCHING! YOUR WHITE PICKETING! YOU'RE NOT GETTING OFF THE HOOK OF HISTORY THAT EASY, BABY!

YOU'RE DYING OF
ROT, WHITEY!
YOUR MEN ARE
AUTOMATONS,
YOUR WOMEN,
DEATH MASKS!
YOU SAY YOU
WANT TO HELP
ME? YOU
CAN'T EVEN HELP
YOURSELF,
WHITEY!

DON'T YOU SEE
HOW I HATE
YOU, WHITEY?
YOU LIBERAL
REFORMERS!
YOU CRIPPLED
POWER
STRUCTURE!
I SCORN
YOU, WHITEY!
I REVILE
YOU!